PUZZLE STORIES

YOU SHOULD SEE MY CAT

Martin Oliver • Sami Sweeten

Hippo

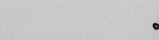

Scholastic Children's Books,
Commonwealth House, 1-19 New Oxford Street,
London, WC1A 1NU, UK
a division of Scholastic Publications Ltd
London ~ New York ~ Toronto ~ Sydney ~ Auckland

First published in the UK by Scholastic Ltd, 1996

Text copyright © Martin Oliver, 1996
Illustrations © Sami Sweeten, 1996

ISBN: 0 590 13390 X

Printed and bound in Hong Kong

10 9 8 7 6 5 4 3 2 1

The right of Martin Oliver and Sami Sweeten to be identified as the author and illustrator
respectively of this work has been asserted by them in accordance with
the Copyright, Designs and Patents Act, 1988.

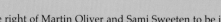

Hello, I'm Claire and this is my cat, Cleo. She's very friendly and loves other animals. Eating and sleeping are her favourite hobbies and she also likes riding in my bicycle basket – unless there is something else she wants to do.

We have lots of fun together. Come with us and you'll see for yourself. There are always plenty of funny and unusual things happening in the places we visit. If you keep your eyes peeled you might spot some of them.

Cleo's favourite things are her pink toy mice. There is one hidden on every double page. Look for them carefully – sometimes they are in the strangest places.

I was feeling hungry when I woke up and pulled the curtains. I always look forward to breakfast and so does Cleo. She visits the neighbours for extra food but she only goes where she is welcome. **You should see which houses she visits.**

After I had eaten my breakfast, I got on to my bike and tried to find Cleo. I knew that she would be asleep but it's hard to find my cat napping. **You should see where she likes to snooze.**

GRO BIG

Cleo jumped into my bicycle basket and we cycled to the harbour. Cleo couldn't wait to get out and explore. The harbour is one of her favourite places, **you should see why Cleo likes it so much.**

It was hard to get Cleo away from the harbour but after a while we cycled inland. I stopped by the river and Cleo leapt off my bike. **You should see her playing ship's cat.**

HAMS
THEATRE
COMPANY

HAMS

We waved goodbye to the boats then headed into town. Cleo knew where she wanted to go. She ran inside the museum. **You should see which section she likes best.**

Soon Cleo decided it was time to leave the museum and I followed her. It was cold outside. I thought my scarf would keep me warm but it didn't. **You should see why.**

I gathered up the remains of my scarf then I began looking for Cleo. I didn't find her until I turned the corner. In amongst the town parade, I spotted Cleo. **You should see her being swept along.**

SOUP

HAMS
THEATRE COMPANY

HOTEL

The parade was great fun but by the time it had gone past Cleo had gone too. I decided to go home. On the way I spotted Cleo playing with her gang. Her best friends are called Snowy, Twirly, Tiger and Domino. **You should see Cleo and her friends.**

I carried on walking. By now it was nearly lunch time and I knew Cleo would be on her way home too. Just then I heard dogs barking but I wasn't worried about Cleo. She always finds a way to avoid them. **You should see her safe route.**

After lunch, I did some colouring while Cleo had a nap. Cleo was still fast asleep on the sofa when I went into the kitchen to fetch some more crayons.

When I walked back into the lounge I noticed that Cleo had gone and she had taken lots of things with her. **You should see what she took.**

Why was Cleo going out in such bad weather? I grabbed my raincoat and umbrella and rushed after her. Splashing through the puddles, I followed Cleo into the park. **You should see where she was heading.**

I was a bit nervous about going inside the old windmill, but when I pushed open the creaky door and saw the things Cleo had taken from our house, I smiled. **You should see why.**

Thanks to Cleo, the animals were soon warm and dry and we all played together inside the windmill. When the rain stopped, Mum arrived to give us a lift home. We waved goodbye but we promised to come back the next day.

I hope you can see why I think Cleo is such a great cat. **Mind you, if you enjoyed the adventures I had with Cleo, you should see the fun I have with my mum.**

DID YOU SEE ...?

PAGES 4/5

Cleo goes to these three houses for extra breakfasts.

You can see Cleo here.

Cleo's toy mouse is here.

Did you see?

A knocked-over plant
A postwoman being chased
A fish fountain
A chimney being swept
A crocodile

PAGES 6/7

Cleo is sleeping here.

Her toy mouse is here.

Did you see?
Claire
A train
Some squirrels
A mole
A giant mouse

PAGES 8/9

Cleo is catching a fish here. That's why she likes the harbour so much.

A toy mouse is hidden here.

Did you see?

Claire
A cat-shaped balloon
A sea-sick sailor
A cat with a fishing rod
An eskimo canoe

29

PAGES 10/11

Cleo is on board this boat.

Her toy mouse is here.

Did you see?
Claire
A lost penguin
A bath-tub
A tangled tent
A waterskier
splashing someone

PAGES 12/13

She has hidden a
toy mouse here.

Cleo is in her favourite
Egyptian section.

Did you see?
Claire
An art thief
Some dinosaur eggs
An unwrapped mummy
A man being prodded
with a spear

PAGES 14/15

Claire's scarf has been
unravelled. If you follow
the trail of wool, you'll find
Cleo at the end of it here.

Cleo's toy mouse is here.

Did you see?
A boy on a skateboard
A birthday cake
A very long scarf
A balloon
A fish mobile

Cleo has hidden a toy mouse here.

Cleo is being swept along on a broomstick.

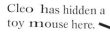

Did you see?
Claire
A pantomime horse
Some fake bats
A broken drum
A singing cat

Cleo is over here.

This is Snowy. He has got white fur.

This is Tiger. She has got tiger stripes on her coat.

This is Twirly. She has got a curly tail.

This is Domino. His coat looks like domino spots.

Cleo's pink toy mouse is hidden under here.

Did you see?
Claire, a cat burglar,
a worried goldfish,
a Jack-in-the-Box,
some mice chasing a cat

Cleo is here.

Her safe route to Claire is marked in black.

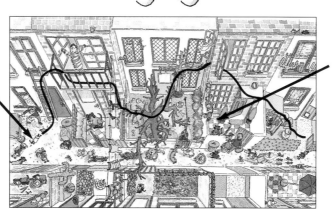

Her toy mouse is here.

Did you see?
A rattlesnake
A cook
A smelly shoe
A vulture
A sundial

PAGES 22/23

If you look closely at the pictures, you will see that Cleo has taken a milk carton, some bowls, a cardigan, a cushion, a packet of choc drops, a knitting basket with balls of wool, her blanket, her basket and the trolley.

Cleo has also moved lots of things. Did you see where she put the Sphinx bookend, the video cassette, a bottle and her toy mouse?

PAGES 24/25

Cleo is heading towards the windmill.

Her toy mouse is here.

Did you see?
Claire
Some children splashing
Some cold and wet animals
A kite
A scuba diver

PAGES 26/27

Cleo is here. She is helping the animals.

Can you see all the things that she brought from Claire's house? They are circled in the picture.

One of her toy mice is here.

Did you see?
Claire
A friendly ghost
A swinging squirrel
A watering can
A mouse on a saddle

PAGE 28

Claire's mum is here.

She is waiting to give Claire and Cleo a lift home in her motorcycle sidecar.